A special thanks
to everyone
who has helped make
Know Yourself
what it is today.

Dear Reader

Knowing yourself is truly the beginning of all wisdom. We give young learners the building blocks they need to start their unique journey of self-discovery: an understanding of human anatomy — literally how we are put together. Knowledge of one's own human body is an empowering context on which anyone can build.

Learning about the body and mind at a young age sets the foundation for honoring one's physical form, develops confidence, and begins the discovery of who we are meant to be in this world.

Now that's real power.

The Know Yourself Team

Quick-Start Guide

Hello Know Yourselfers!

Follow these steps to start a new journey and explore the integumentary system. Have fun on this Self Literacy quest, and remember - knowing yourself is more than skin-deep!

1

Grab your breakfast and sunscreen. We're going to Oakland, California!

It's fascinating to see just how much things can change across time! We are going to take you through some U.S. history, from the founding and early days, up until the late 1960s.

2

Read Time Skaters Adventure 12.

Pinky and Shorty are staying right where they are this time, though the 'when' is still changing. Find out what happens when they visit their hometown's past!

3

Get equipped!

Search for your supplies listed on the home inventory page. If you need help finding something, don't be afraid to ask for help. We're all part of a community!

Table of Contents

Hello Adventurer!

Welcome to Adventure 12 - The Integumentary System.

In this workbook, you will learn about the United States in the 1960s, and visit Oakland, California and learn about your body's integumentary system. There will be information to read, activities to complete, and quizzes to take when you are ready to challenge yourself! Take your time along the way - spend as much or as little time as you like on each activity.

Good luck, and have fun!

Can you find **Oakland, California?**

THE TIME TRAVEL CLOCK READS

1967

Get ready for a hair-raising adventure!

LEARN ABOUT

The Integumentary System

Your body's first line of defense is more than meets the eye!

VISIT

U.S.A., 1960s

Tensions rise as the struggle for equality and opportunity continues.

MEET

Kwame Brathwaite and Elombe Brath

The photographers and innovators of the Black is Beautiful movement.

No sweat!*

That means "**no problem!**"
You might already know this expression, which originated in the 1960s (and has a little bit to do with the body system you are learning).

*Say it like this: "noh SWET"

The strongest syllable is shown in **CAPITALS** and **red**.

Don't miss
this last adventure...

Time Skaters Adventure 12
If I Could Derm Back Time

How are you feeling, Naz? I know the multiple time jumps are unprecedented...

I think my brain is just catching up to the fact that we were in an actual **war**.

We're just glad you're home safe!

Bounski! I need you to focus your telekinesis on the Skelehub!

Sorry, Bounski just got caught up in the moment.

It's just as I suspected!

"The portal is growing stronger, not just due to your presence..."

"...but also because of your connection to one another!"

Meanwhile...

"This tastes funny!"

"Hey, I can hear Stokely!"

"Shocker, he's on his fifth meal of the day."

"Your ears have the right idea, Shorty."

"Let's bring Stokely in on this."

"Holy hologram phone, Batman."

Ahhhhhhhhhh!

What's wrong, Stokely baby?

Oh, is this a hologram? Phones really have gotten fancy.

Hey, Grandma Peg.

Hi, Shorty. Have fun with your li'l friends. Y'all stay outta trouble now!

It looks like the Skelehub has picked our new destination.

But that's Oakland. We're already here!

It's not just a question of where, but when.

Are you ready for another trip?

I think I need a break from time travel.

Plus, I want to decipher this message from **Dr. B.**

It's weird. The portal seems more stable than ever before.

But it kind of feels kind of...

Creepy?

Yeah. I almost wonder if we should turn...

...back.

And the door back to the lab disappears. Totally not terrifying.

Guess our only option is to move forward.

CLICK

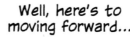

Well, here's to moving forward...

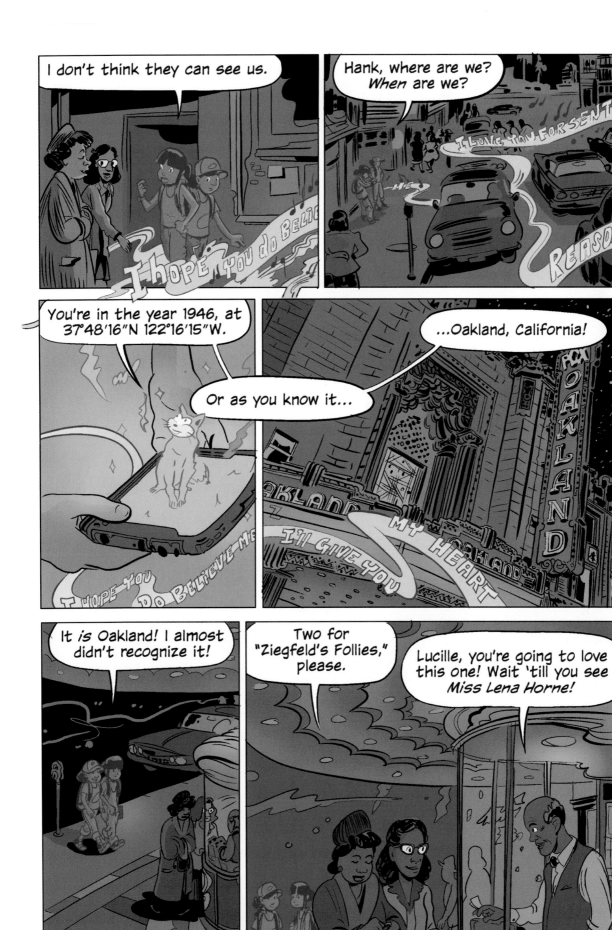

Oh, Mama! She's so glamorous!

I'd love to have hair like hers.

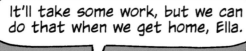

It'll take some work, but we can do that when we get home, Ella.

Of course, this will all be easier once I have my beauty parlor up and running.

You let me know when you open that beauty parlor, Lucille!

I'll send the missus your way!

HAIR HAIR, EVERYWHERE

You wash and brush your hair, but what does your hair do for you?

Eyebrows and eyelashes help keep sweat, debris, and pathogens from getting into your eyes, and shield your eyes from the sun. Eyelashes help keep the eyes moist.

Little hairs inside your nose and ears catch particles and pathogens and keep your nasal passages and ear canals clean.

The hair on your head helps warm and protect your scalp. However, lots of people also use hair styles to express their unique personality. What do you express about yourself with your hairstyle?

Each strand of hair starts inside a follicle, a small tube inside your skin. That's where the root of your hair lives. Tiny blood vessels at the base of each follicle feed your hair so it forms new cells-that's your hair growing!

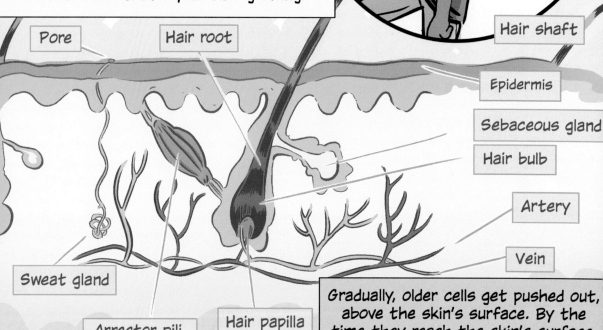

Pore

Hair root

Hair shaft

Epidermis

Sebaceous gland

Hair bulb

Artery

Vein

Sweat gland

Arrector pili muscle

Hair papilla

Gradually, older cells get pushed out, above the skin's surface. By the time they reach the skin's surface, cells in the upper part of the hair, the shaft, are no longer alive.

ENOUGH TO MAKE YOUR HAIR CURL

Why is some hair straight and some hair curly? It's all in your follicles.

Hair is made of protein fibers called **keratin**. Sometimes, while your hair is still in the follicle, chemical bonds form, causing the fibers to cling together.

The shape of the follicle determines whether hair is curly or straight. A round follicle produces straight hair. An oval follicle produces wavy or curly hair. The flatter the oval, the curlier the hair. This happens because the fibers in hair bump up against each other more oval-shaped follicles, and more chemical bonds form.

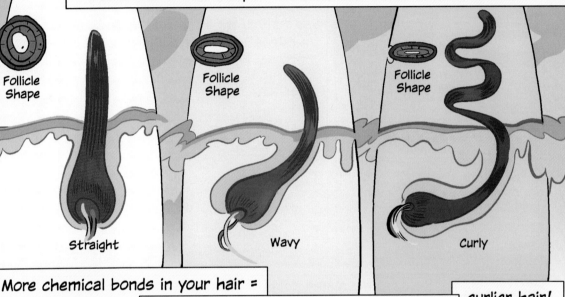

Follicle Shape — Straight

Follicle Shape — Wavy

Follicle Shape — Curly

More chemical bonds in your hair =

more protein fibers sticking together =

curlier hair!

People with straight hair have round, straight follicles, and people with curly hair have oval-shaped, curvier follicles.

Whoa!

Now Hair This! If your hair naturally becomes curlier when it's humid outside, it's because the hydrogen molecules in water are bonding with your hair!

Now this looks more like the Oakland I know!

Except we're underdressed.

We're definitely not back in our own time.

Why are we making multiple time jumps?

Last time, we were following Chester. So this time--

Hey! New girl!

Huh?

Your mama don't know how to use a hot comb?

My Mama could fix that for you.

Fix it? There's nothing wrong with--

MAr-gA-ret!!

What's wrong, Roland?

It's almost five. We're going to miss "Cosmic Voyager"!

Hey, I've seen this place.

My great-great-grandma started this shop.

Your great-great-grandmother is Lucille? The woman from 1946?

Yeah, and that means Margaret...

...is my Grandma Peg.

Can we watch "Cosmic Voyager" in here? Please?

I don't know, Margaret. These ladies didn't come in here for--

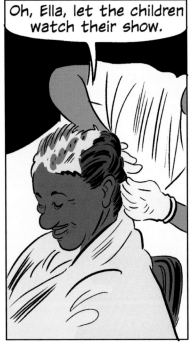

Oh, Ella, let the children watch their show.

Any show set in the future is fine by me.

Especially this one - the captain reminds me of my grandson!

Alright, but don't get too rowdy in here.

We won't!

Come on, Ma. Someone has to be first. Why not Margaret?

I want to travel through time! I just worry the technology is too far off.

Actually--

Mmpf!

Maybe *you* could invent the technology!

Maybe I will!

Thanks, Shorty. I got a little excited.

It's starting!

Journeying among the stars for all humanity...

...Cosmic Voyager!

KEN VEGAS AS CAPTAIN CHUCK

Ooh, the pink Furzots and the green Furzots! This is my favorite episode!

You've seen this episode? But it's brand new!

Um...

SMACK!

Oh, she doesn't seem to mind!

I don't mind at all!

Besides everyone that visits our shop becomes a part of the family!

You all make it so welcoming here!

And hello, Mama.

What's with the gloves? You going to the opera or something?

Franklin, that hair of yours has gone wild.

I prefer to think of it as gone natural.

It can be natural and cleaned up, too. Sit.

Thanks, sis. I'd be lost without you.

Uh-huh. Lost in your hair.

There she is!

Lt. Umoja!

She's amazing. Can you imagine speaking 175 languages like she does?

When I'm an astronaut, I'll need hair like that!

But that's not how all black women wear their hair in the future!

Pinky, a lot of people now don't like the word "Black."

Oh!

Aww, don't sweat it, my brown sister.

NATIONAL GEOGRAPHIC

Have you seen Kwame Brathwaite's photos? They remind us that "Black is Beautiful."

Photos like that are changing the times!

Anyway, that's not Umoja's hair.

It's a wig. Probably a very expensive wig, but that certainly didn't grow out of her scalp.

What?! How can you tell?

A professional can always tell.

You know how they've got special effects makeup?

Well, they've got special effects hair, too.

And there's no bigger special effect than Captain Chuck's toupee!

Ella, you are too much!

You know, Ida's home from Spelman.

Maybe you could swing by for dinner.

Much appreciated, but Shirley and I are real solid. I don't think she'd take too kindly to me having a dinner date with your Ida.

Where is our future Madam President?

Hey, baby. Ella's making me beautiful.

I see that.

I'm jealous. I wish I could grow an afro like yours.

Your hair looks like that naturally?

More or less.

Girl, you're lucky. You've got that good hair!

Hey, if it covers your head, it's good hair.

Check out that girl with the puffs! Her hair's out of sight!

No reason for folks to fry and bleach and straighten what nature gave them.

Careful with that talk! There's nothing wrong with coming to get your hair done!

And this "natural hair" nonsense is going to put us out of business!

Ouch!

CRASH!

Ma!

Skin DEEP

Your hair, along with your skin and nails, makes up your **integumentary*** system. Each of these covers your internal body parts and performs its own special job.

Together, they make sure the body is well protected from injury and infection, functioning as a physical barrier from pathogens.

The main organ of this system is your skin. It keeps everything together!

Let us in!

Goodbye forever!

Microbes

KNOCK!

'Sup. I'm new here.

Skin cell

As the largest organ on your body, it's your first line of defense against foreign invaders.

Basale layer

Epidermis

So are we.

Your skin is a living organ, made of many skin cells. Each and every day your body sheds skin cells and makes new ones to replace what you shed. Your skin produces about 30,000 new cells every 60 seconds!

Hair shaft

Your skin is made of two distinct layers:
The **epidermis*** is the part of the skin you can see. The **dermis*** is hidden underneath.

Sebaceous gland

Dermis

Hair follicle

Hair bulb

Hair papilla

*Say it like this: in-teg-yoo-MEN-tuh-ree, eh-pih-DUR-mis, DUR-mis

Your **sweat glands** are on autopilot and release a little bit of sweat all the time. The sweat travels up through your **pores.**

When you get hot, your sweat glands release more sweat, cooling down your skin. When your body gets cold, your arrector pili muscles engage, making your hairs stand up straight up. In furry animals like cats, this creates a layer of air that lets their fur retain more heat. Since humans don't have much hair on our bodies, we get goosebumps!

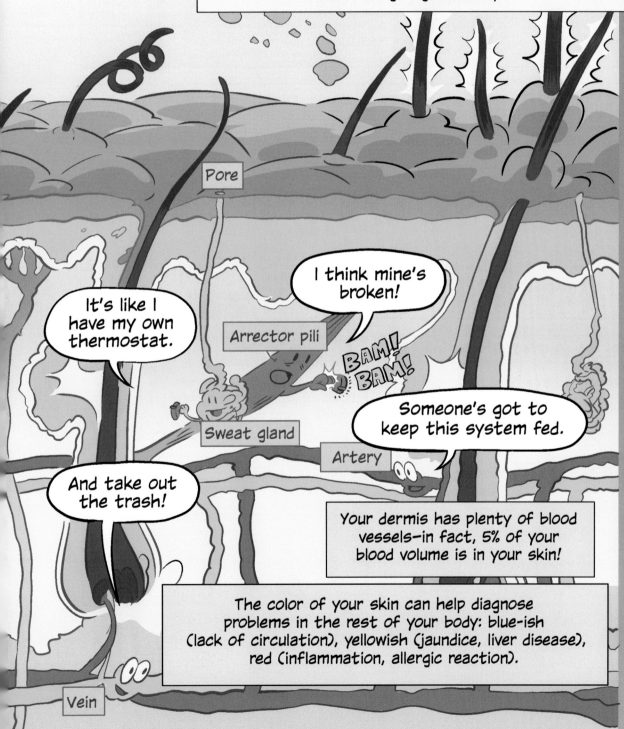

Your dermis has plenty of blood vessels—in fact, 5% of your blood volume is in your skin!

The color of your skin can help diagnose problems in the rest of your body: blue-ish (lack of circulation), yellowish (jaundice, liver disease), red (inflammation, allergic reaction).

You are a miracle worker, Ella!

How much do I owe you?

Do you think other women would pay for something like this?

You bet! I bet they'd pay for you to take care of their afros like Franklin's, too.

Then just tell them to come here! That's payment enough.

You're amazing, sis. Have a good night!

What are you on about, Ella?

This is an amazing business opportunity, Mama!

Not just afros, but braids, too!

There are so many different hairstyles out there—and we can create our own!

That's a great idea!

We can shift our focus!

We can stop using those toxic chemicals we have been using for years.

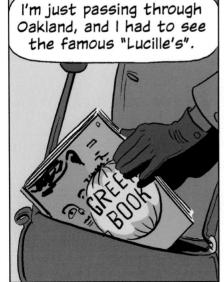

Now I'm here visiting an old friend.

Wow! What an adventure!

Well, you should get your dad to take you on a roadtrip!

Oh. My dad passed away last year.

Oh, did that already happen?

I mean, how tragic, to lose your father at such a young age.

What's up, Pinky?

Something about that woman's story seems familiar...

It almost makes you wish you could turn back time, doesn't it?

Heh, we were just talking about time travel today.

Oh! Hank! Have you decoded the message?

We've got bigger problems, Pinky.

RASH COURSE

Have you ever found yourself with an itchy, flaky, or painful rash? That's called **dermatitis,*** and a lot of different things can cause it: pollution, bacteria, a problem with your immune system, and even certain kinds of fungi.

A rash you get from something you touch is called **contact dermatitis.** If you're allergic to a plant, food, or material (like poison ivy, peanuts, or latex), your skin reacts by turning red, swelling up, and sometimes even cracking or oozing. This may make you feel self-conscious, but don't worry-dermatitis isn't contagious!

Some chemicals can irritate skin. The acid that leaks from old batteries and bleach, for example, can leave a painful rash.

Even soap and water can irritate your skin if you have lots and lots of contact with them. Washing your hands too often can dry them out-think about how the skin around your lips cracks if you lick them too much in the winter.

Scrub Scrub!

Some people might be more prone to dermatitis because of their jobs, like hairstylists, who regularly handle products like bleaches, dyes, and hair straighteners.

Some hair straighteners contain lye, a chemical that can burn holes in skin! That's why it's important for people who use harsh chemicals to protect their skin and use gloves.

*Say it like this: der-muh-TIE-tis

My Name is Prints

If you look at the tips of your fingers, you'll see a series of tiny ridges in your epidermis that form swirling patterns. Those are your fingerprints, and each fingerprint is one of a kind!

Almost every person on Earth is born with a unique set of fingerprints.* When you touch an object, sweat and oil on your fingers ends up on that object, leaving behind an impression of your fingerprint. That means if someone has a record of your fingerprints, they can identify objects that you have touched!

Many people rely on their unique fingerprints every day. Have you ever unlocked a phone with your fingerprint? Have you ever paid for something by touching your finger to an electronic pad? By reading your fingerprint, those devices know that you are you and not someone else.

Fingerprints have a lot of other uses, too. Some employers fingerprint their employees for security purposes. In many countries, people vote with their fingerprints. Fingerprints have been used to identify missing people—even people who can't remember who they are. And fingerprints are used to solve mysteries!

*A few people have been born with a condition called **adermatoglyphia,*** which prevents them from developing any fingerprints at all!

*Say it like this: ah-der-ma-toe-GLIF-ee-ah

Cough

Lucille and Ella! They're trapped in amber!

So is Margaret!

Why aren't **you** frozen?!

Because...

...I've been searching for Dr. Bonyfide.

And now I've finally found him!

Pinky! Shorty! I'm opening the portal now!

Come back to the lab and bring Roland with you!

You heard the cat! Come on!

I'm not going anywhere without Margaret!

Did you know that everywhere you go, you leave a little piece of yourself behind?

Hair, fingerprints, bits of skin, microscopic strands of DNA.

Everywhere the Time Skaters went, I picked up a souvenir.

I thought I could make a device that would let me control my journey through time.

Alas, all this trinket does is freeze time. And some people are immune.

It seems I'm still missing one ingredient: you.

THE INTEGUMENTARY SYSTEM

THE INTEGUMENTARY SYSTEM

Learning Calendar

Part 1
Know Your History

Estimated hours **4.5** *hours* *of fun*

Locate the United States (bonus points for Oakland, CA) on a world map using a globe, an atlas or an online map (like this one: knowyourself.com/maps).

Read the comic **Time Skaters Adventure 12: If I Could Derm Back Time**.

Gather the adventure equipment you will need on pages 44 through 46.

Travel back to *United States, 1960s.*

Compete with *Contradictory Cubes.*

Nourish your body and mind in *Building Breakfast.*

Comb through *Know Your Hairstyles.*

Brush through *Know Your Art.*

Demonstrate in *Know Your Language.*

Tackle *Operation Oakland.*

Part 2
Know Your Integumentary System

Get beyond the skin in *Know Your Integumentary System.*

Pore over *Know Your Skin.*

Absorb *Know Your Melanin.*

Get calculating in *Know Your Surface Area.*

Test your limits in *Know Your Sensitivity.*

Become an integumentary detective in *Know Your Fingerprints*.

Take a closer look at *Mole Patrol* and *Acne Acumen*.

Unravel a *Strand at Hand*.

Overcome the *Integumentary Investigation*.

Surge through *Systems Security*.

Part **3**

Know Your Appetite

Build up your hunger with *Know Your Appetite*.

Read the recipes on the following pages. Make a shopping list, purchase ingredients, and get your kitchen ready!

Prepare *Hoppin' John* and *Lemon Sour Cream Pound Cake*.

Share your dishes with your family.
Discuss *Thoughts for Young Chefs* around the table!

Part **4**

Show What You Know!

Impress with *Positively Powerful*.

Explore more with *Further Reading*.

Home Inventory Checklist

Ask your parents to help you find these items around the house. These are some of the tools you will need on your adventure.

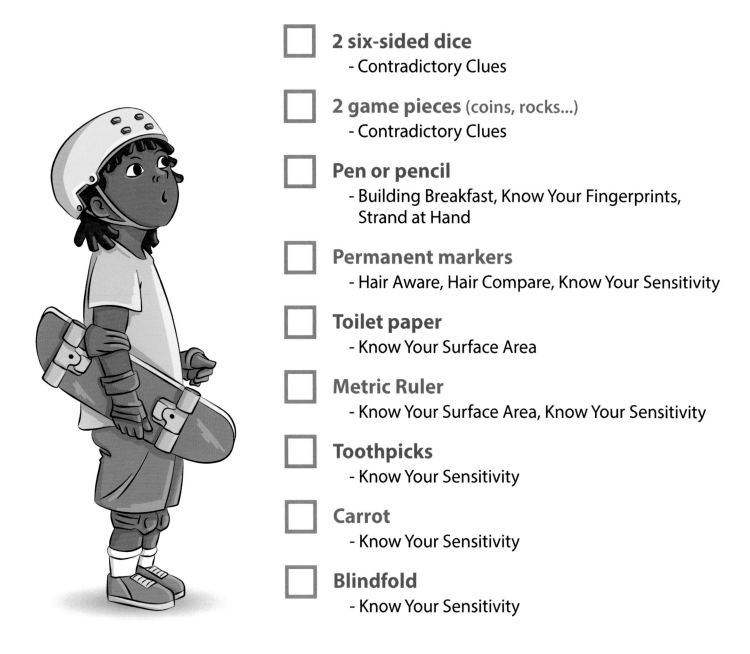

- [ ] **2 six-sided dice**
  - Contradictory Clues

- [ ] **2 game pieces** (coins, rocks...)
  - Contradictory Clues

- [ ] **Pen or pencil**
  - Building Breakfast, Know Your Fingerprints, Strand at Hand

- [ ] **Permanent markers**
  - Hair Aware, Hair Compare, Know Your Sensitivity

- [ ] **Toilet paper**
  - Know Your Surface Area

- [ ] **Metric Ruler**
  - Know Your Surface Area, Know Your Sensitivity

- [ ] **Toothpicks**
  - Know Your Sensitivity

- [ ] **Carrot**
  - Know Your Sensitivity

- [ ] **Blindfold**
  - Know Your Sensitivity

- [ ] **White cardstock paper**
  - Know Your Fingerprints

- [ ] **Black ink pad**
  - Know Your Fingerprints

- [ ] **Clear glass jar**
  - Know Your Fingerprints

- [ ] **Glass cleaner**
  - Know Your Fingerprints

- [ ] **Paper towel**
  - Know Your Fingerprints

- [ ] **Gloves**
  - Know Your Fingerprints

- [ ] **Cookie or other treat**
  - Know Your Fingerprints

- [ ] **Notecards** (sized 4 x 6 inches)
  - Know Your Fingerprints

- [ ] **Bowl or hat**
  - Know Your Fingerprints

Home Inventory Checklist

☐ **Feathered paint brush**
- Know Your Fingerprints

☐ **Charcoal sticks**
- Know Your Fingerprints

☐ **Cellophane tape**
- Know Your Fingerprints

☐ **Magnifying glass**
- Mole Patrol, Acne Acumen, Strand at Hand

☐ **Highly magnified mirror**
- Mole Patrol, Acne Acumen

☐ **Ziploc® bag**
- Strand at Hand

☐ **Paperclip**
- Strand at Hand

☐ **A strand of your hair**
- Strand at Hand

☐ **Tape**
- Strand at Hand

☐ **Pennies**
- Strand at Hand

☐ **Paper**
- Strand at Hand

> ✓ Be sure to check the items off when you've found them.

coloring opportunity

Know Your History

United States, 1960s

The 1960s was a decade of change in all aspects of life from music, attitudes, and society as a whole. Many were fighting for themselves and others to gain equal rights.

The Civil Rights Movement

The **Civil Rights Movement** was one example of the fight for equal rights for Black Americans. While the Civil War abolished slavery, it did not end **discrimination***
against Black people. Instead, they continued to be treated poorly, particularly in southern states.

*****Say it like this:

discrimination - "dis-crim-eh-**NATION**"

The strongest syllable is always shown in **CAPITALS** and **red**.

For a long time in the United States, laws kept people *segregated** based on race. Even though the law said that everyone should get equal treatment, some states and cities decided that they could give people different treatment if they claimed the treatment was equal.

For example, if people from both groups had a school to attend, that counted as equal - even if one school was much nicer than the other. Many people could see that these **"separate but equal"** rules were not actually fair, but it was not until 1954 that the Supreme Court said they were illegal.

Even after that, fighting against segregation lasted decades, and in some places is still going on today.

*Segregation

The separation or isolation of a race, class, or ethnic group by restrictions on where they live, by separate educational facilities, or by other discriminatory means.

Know Your History

What happened?

Life in the South was difficult for African American citizens. Local governments passed Laws that made it impossible for Black citizens to vote, and Jim Crow laws kept Whites and Blacks segregated and made life for Black Americans much more difficult, excluding them from high-quality education, vital resources, and voting rights.

Between 1915 and 1970, more than 6 million African Americans left the South and moved to non-segregated parts of the Northern and Western states to escape this cruel and unfair treatment.

This mass movement from south to north is known as **the Great Migration***.

***Say it like this:**

migration - **"my-GRAY-shin"**

The strongest syllable is always shown in **CAPITALS** and **red**.

The Great Migration led to new and better-paying jobs opening up in cities like New York, Philadelphia, Chicago, Detroit, Los Angeles, and even smaller cities like Oakland. African-American families decided to leave the South for better opportunities and more fair treatment.

Oakland, CA

During the Great Migration, many people went to Oakland, California. Oakland had a thriving port and became a centerpiece of Black culture and the fight for equal rights. Oakland saw the rise of historic district Seventh Street; which had many Black owned businesses and drew great attention from famous international musicians. This also became one of the centers for the fight for Civil Rights, with many influential leaders and community organizations having their roots in Oakland.

Contradictory Clues

In *Know Your History* you learned about the history of segregation in the United States, and the important role which fairness has played throughout American history. You learned that when there are rules in place that benefit one group of people but put another group of people at a disadvantage, that this is an example of unfairness. Likewise, you learned that when unfair rules are in place, there will be some who attempt to argue that the rules are fair, even though they are not.

Finally, you learned what justice is:

justice is when unfair rules are made fair — when the rules equally benefit and equally disadvantage everyone.

Time to put your history skills to the test!

Play the Contradictory Cubes game to see an example of how rules can say they are being fair while not being truly fair at all.

Contradictory Cubes

Materials:

- **Two six-sided dice**

- **The Contradictory Cubes Game** (page 55)

- **Two game pieces** (coins, rocks, or anything you want to use)

- **Two players**

Directions:

1. Place both game pieces on the start square.

2. Player 1 rolls one die and moves ahead the number of spaces the die says.

3. Player 2 rolls both dice, then picks one. They move the number of spaces the picked die says.

4. If you land on a space from your roll, do what it says on that space.

5. The first player to get to the End square wins the game.

Directions:

6. Switch which person is Player 1 and which is Player 2, and play again.

7. Talk about your experience playing the game afterwards.

   a. **What made the game seem fair?**

   _____

   _____

   _____

   b. **What made it unfair?**

   _____

   _____

   _____

   c. **How did it feel to be Player 1, and how did it feel to be Player 2?**

   _____

   _____

   _____

Contradictory Cubes Game

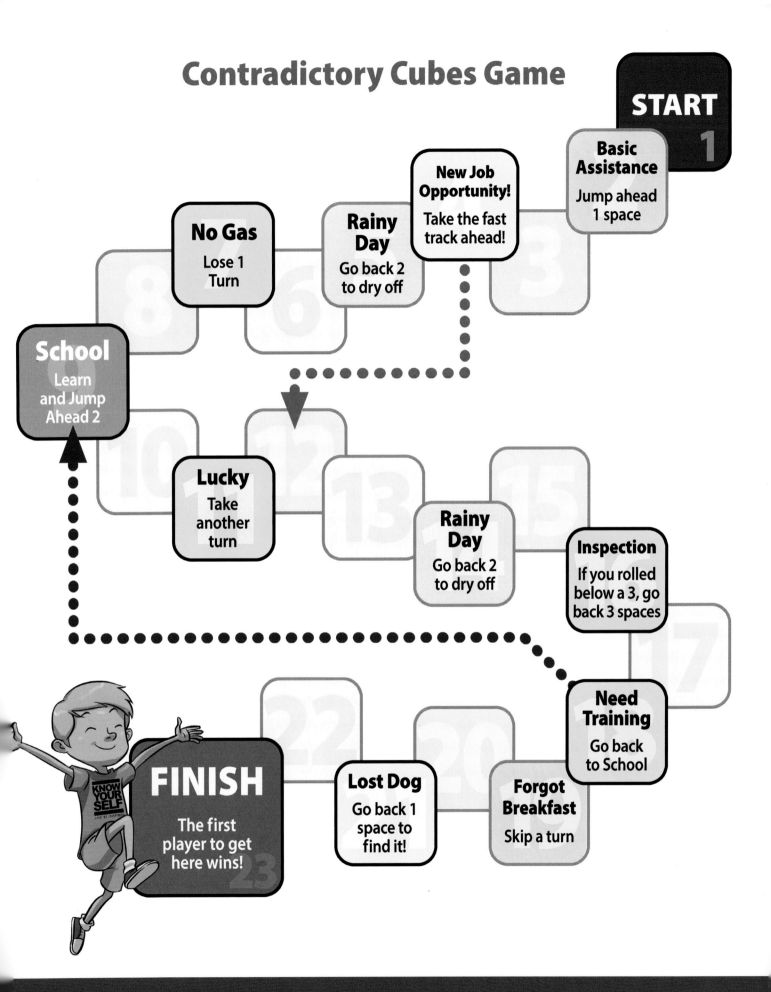

START 1

Basic Assistance Jump ahead 1 space

New Job Opportunity! Take the fast track ahead!

Rainy Day Go back 2 to dry off

No Gas Lose 1 Turn

School Learn and Jump Ahead 2

Lucky Take another turn

Rainy Day Go back 2 to dry off

Inspection If you rolled below a 3, go back 3 spaces

Need Training Go back to School

FINISH The first player to get here wins!

Lost Dog Go back 1 space to find it!

Forgot Breakfast Skip a turn

Free Breakfast for Children Program

In 1969, one of the most influential community programs in all of U.S. history was formed — the **Free Breakfast for Children Program**. At the time, most poor children went to school hungry and, as a result, could not focus in class. Without proper nutrition, our ability to process information and learn new things becomes severely impaired. At the time, the National School Lunch Program provided children with reduced-price food at school, but not free food as we see in public schools today. As a result, many children were still unable to eat enough to hold them over for a whole school day.

Working with St. Augustine's Church in Oakland, parents, community members, and businesses donated food and prepared it for the children who needed breakfast before school.

Programs like this were influential and helped the general public realize the importance of keeping children well-fed while in school. Nutrition is crucial to development, both physically and educationally.

The Free Breakfast for Children Program was so influential that the federal government expanded the National School Lunch Program.

This expansion provided children with free lunches, and it created the National School Breakfast program for the entirety of the U.S., which now offers both reduced and free breakfasts in schools depending on income level.

Building Breakfast

"Breakfast is the most important meal of the day."

You've probably been told that for your entire life.
But do you know why breakfast is the most important meal of the day?

When you wake up in the morning, your body peaks in its production of the stress hormone known as **cortisol***. The longer we go without energy from food, the more tired and less focused you may feel because not eating prolongs your early-morning elevated cortisol levels. In other words, not eating breakfast literally makes you more stressed out during the daytime!

Eating breakfast will jump start your day, giving you the energy and vital nutrients that you need to stay and feel healthy. Not to mention that it's hard to focus or feel good when all you can think about is food!

***Say it like this:**

cortisol - "kor-tuh-**SAAL**"

The strongest syllable is always shown in **CAPITALS** and **red**.

With all of that in mind, here is how you can build your own breakfast to jump start your day!

The best way to find out how your breakfast affects you is to track it!

Materials:

- **Blank copy of the breakfast chart** (on page 63)

- **Pen or Pencil**

Building Breakfast

Directions:

1. Each morning, write down what you eat. Check if your food includes protein, carbohydrates, or fat. Use your **Macronutrient Matrix** to estimate if you aren't sure what's in your breakfast.

2. Wait an hour, then think about how you are feeling. Have you been able to focus? Are you feeling tired?

3. Make a note about how you are doing on the chart.

4. A few minutes before you eat lunch, think about how you are feeling again and make another note.

5. After a week, see if you can find a pattern. Does eating different breakfast foods make you feel differently?
Is it harder to focus before lunch when you eat a high-sugar breakfast or a high-protein breakfast?

Protein

Fat

Carbohydrates

Macronutrient Matrix

	JOBS	FOCUS ON		LIMIT
CARBOHYDRATES	Primary fuel for the body	Whole grains	Beans	Sugar
	Provides energy to move and think	Vegetables	Fruit	Refined flour
PROTEIN	Provides structure for tissue	Lentils, Beans		Processed meats
	Involved in metabolic, hormonal and enzyme systems	Soy products	Whole grains	Red meat
		Nuts, Seeds	Animal protein	
FAT	Energy reserve	Vegetable oils	Avocado	Fried food
	Aids in absorptions and transport of vitamins	Fatty fish	Nuts, Seeds	Packaged baked goods

Building Breakfast Chart (example)

	Breakfast	Protein (P) Carbohydrates (C) Fat (F)	Morning Notes	Lunch Notes
SUNDAY	1 egg, banana, toast	P, C, F	Felt good	Hungry but feeling okay
MONDAY	Cereal	C	Tired	Very tired and hungry
TUESDAY	Eggs and bacon	P	More awake but hungry	
WEDNESDAY	Apple and Cereal	C		
THURSDAY				
FRIDAY				
SATURDAY				

Building Breakfast Chart

	Breakfast	Protein (P) Carbohydrates (C) Fat (F)	Morning Notes	Lunch Notes
SUNDAY				
MONDAY				
TUESDAY				
WEDNESDAY				
THURSDAY				
FRIDAY				
SATURDAY				

Know Your Hairstyles

Get Out of My Hair

Changes in hairstyles over the years and around the world tell a lot about places, history, and people. As we have learned, the 60s brought major changes to fashion and beauty that we still talk about today.

Beehive

Created to shake up the world of beauty, Chicago hairstylist Margaret Vinci Heldt, created the Beehive. This style was inspired by a square hat, called a fez. Heldt wanted a hairstyle that fit under the hat, but when it was taken off the hairstyle would still be there. To create this look, hair is combed backward on top of the head to create a conical shape (think beehive). The outside is then lightly brushed to create a smoothed outer finish.

Mop Top Haircuts

Influenced by musicians of the time, the mop-top became one of the most popular hairstyles for men in the 1960s. This hairstyle included combing hair down towards the eyebrow, allowing the hair to cover the forehead. This style varied slightly from person to person, and variations of it can still be seen today!

Afros

Before the 1960s it was quite common that many African American women straightened their hair with hot combs, chemicals and more. While other styles existed, straight hair became a societal norm. In the early 1900s Madam C. J. Walker popularized the press-and-curl style, and started selling her own line of hair care products made for Black women's hair. Walker went on to build a sales empire, set up beauty schools that trained tens of thousands of Black women as sales agents, and eventually became the first Black woman millionaire in America.

In the 1960s the Afro began to grow in popularity. An Afro is a hairstyle in which naturally curly hair is styled to stand around the head, often in a circular shape. As the Civil Rights Movement grew, it brought a new sense of identity to the African American community. The Afro was adopted and worn by both men and women.

No matter how you choose to wear your hair, it's one of the many things that makes you, you.

Hair Aware, Hair Compare

Many factors contribute to the popularity of certain hairstyles at different times.

What hairstyles do you think are popular today?

Try drawing a few of them here!

Do you have one of those hairstyles yourself?

Now ask your parents, grandparents, or other older relatives what hairstyles were popular when they were young. Ask them to draw a picture of one or two of them.

Finally, ask your parents to help you find a printed photo of yourself that's okay to draw on. Using permanent markers, draw one of the hairstyles your relatives had on yourself.

How does it look?

 Submit your drawings on social media or on knowyourself.com
for a chance to be featured!

#KnowYourAdventure

 KnowYourselfOAK   **KnowYourselfOAK**

Know Your Art

Revolution-hairy

Photographer **Kwame Brathwaite**, along with his activist brother **Elombe Brath** and their Co-founded group AJASS (African Jazz Arts Society and Studios), wanted to popularize the idea that "**Black is Beautiful.**" As we learned in *Know Your Hairstyles*, Afros began to grow in popularity and became a symbol of activism, empowerment, and self-love. During the 1960s and 1970s, Brathwaite photographed Black women, often with dark skin and unstraightened hair, wearing African-inspired fashion. These portraits celebrate the models' innate beauty, and inspired many Black women to embrace their natural skin and hair.

In this picture from the Black is Beautiful exhibition, the woman in the photo is one of the Grandassa models, who paved the way for African-inspired fashion and hairstyles.

* Credit: Sikolo Brathwaite, Grandassa Model © Kwame Brathwaite 1968

Music Revolution

Also during this time music began to change and form new genres and variations, which put down roots for the music that we hear today.

One genre that saw major growth was **rock music**. Rock music grew into many sub genres, each having their own style and purpose, which changed the course of rock music forever. One example is The Beatles, a British rock band which found major success in the United States. The Beatles were at the top of the charts for most of the 60s and continue to hold many musical records to this day. Jimi Hendrix also revolutionized rock music and was responsible for many major innovations in the art of guitar playing — including using various effects to create unique guitar solos and blending genres like blues, rock, and soul music.

The 1960s saw the growth of many African American artists as the civil rights act outlawed discrimination. This paved the way for many African American musicians to become mainstream artists. Artists such as Ray Charles, Aretha Franklin, and Sam Cooke pioneered the creation and growth of **soul music**, without which the R&B (Rhythm and Blues) *music of today may have never been*. Motown Records, a famous recording label, popularized soul music with artists such as The Supremes and the Temptations who were major influences on modern pop music.

Know Your Language

Language is our primary tool for communicating with each other. However, the meaning of words changes over time. Specifically, the meaning of words changes depending on how people are using certain words. There are endless ways in which language has changed in this way.

Here are a few examples of phrases used in the 1960s which we no longer use in the 21st century.

- **"That was a gas!"**
  This meant that you had a good time at an event.

- **"That's boss!"**
  This meant what we mean now by *"cool."* Something fun, exciting, or awesome.

- **"I dig it."**
  This either meant that you understood something, or it meant that you liked something.

- **"Jazzed."**
  This meant the same thing as when we now say "*excited.*"

- **"Groovy."**
  This meant the same thing as what we now mean by *"cool"* as well!

Can you think of some common 'slang' words or phrases that we use today? Write them down and try to define them.

_____

_____

_____

_____

How well do you think these expressions will stand the test of time?

_____

_____

_____

_____

Operation Oakland

After you finish, check the answer key on page 128.

Across:

5. This popular hairstyle was a tall cone-shaped hairstyle on the top of the head.

6. The Free Breakfast Program was founded here.

7. The state Oakland is located in _____ .

8. The time period when more than 6 million Black Americans left the South for other parts of the U.S.

10. Another way to say no problem.

Down:

1. The meal that started the Free Lunch Program.

2. America's first female self-made millionaire.

3. When traits like hair texture or skin color is used to treat people unfairly, it is _____ .

4. One of the photographers who made the Black is Beautiful program popular.

9. Made whites and non-whites racially divided in schools, churches, and other places.

Know Your Integumentary System

Defense Mechanism

You have systems inside your body, but did you know that you're covered in a body system?

Your hair, skin, and nails make up the **integumentary system**.

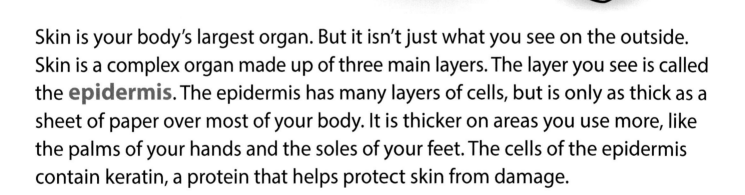

Skin is your body's largest organ. But it isn't just what you see on the outside. Skin is a complex organ made up of three main layers. The layer you see is called the **epidermis**. The epidermis has many layers of cells, but is only as thick as a sheet of paper over most of your body. It is thicker on areas you use more, like the palms of your hands and the soles of your feet. The cells of the epidermis contain keratin, a protein that helps protect skin from damage.

CELL-BY DATE: Cells in the epidermis are replaced every two to four weeks. Nails are replaced every six months. Hair on your head is replaced every two to seven years.

The **dermis** lies beneath the epidermis. It is a thicker than the epidermis and contains two main proteins, **collagen*** and **elastin,*** which make skin flexible and help support the epidermis. The dermis contains many smaller structures, including blood vessels, nerve cells, hair follicles, muscle fibers, oil glands, and sweat glands.

The deepest layer of skin is the **subcutaneous*** layer, which is made up mostly of fat cells.

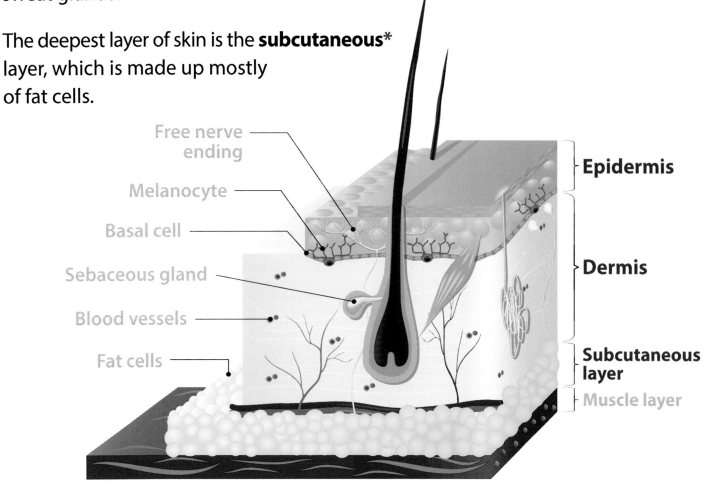

Free nerve ending

Melanocyte

Basal cell

Sebaceous gland

Blood vessels

Fat cells

Epidermis

Dermis

Subcutaneous layer

Muscle layer

***Say them like this:**

collagen - "**CALL**-uh-jin"

elastin - "ih-**LAS**-tin"

subcutaneous - "sub-cue-**TAY**-nee-us"

The strongest syllable is always shown in **CAPITALS** and **red**.

Know Your Integumentary System

The integumentary system has several important functions:

Protection

Skin helps keep pathogens, like bacteria, out of the body. Hairs around your eyes and inside your nose also help keep pathogens out. Fat in the subcutaneous layer protects other organs and pads bones and joints. Pigment in skin and hair offers some protection from sunlight. Nails protect the tips of fingers and toes.

Temperature regulation

Fat cells in the subcutaneous layer help insulate the body. When you're cold, **arrector pili**,* tiny muscles attached to the base of hair follicles, contract. This makes your hair stand up, trapping warm air next to the skin. When you're hot, sweat glands release extra sweat to help cool the body.

Sensing your environment

Skin contains different kinds of nerve cells. **Mechanoreceptors** sense pressure and vibration. **Thermoreceptors** detect changes in temperature. **Nociceptors*** detect pain caused by cuts and scrapes, extreme temperatures, and chemicals.

Waste removal

Even when you aren't hot, sweat glands produce small amounts of sweat, which contains waste materials like urea and salts.

*Say them like this:

arrector pili - "uh-**REK**-tuhr **PIE**-lie"
nociceptors - "**NO**-sih-sep-tors"

The strongest syllable is always shown in **CAPITALS** and **red**.

Know Your Integumentary System

The integumentary system works with other body systems to help maintain homeostasis. Some ways the system interacts with other body systems include:

THE INTEGUMENTARY SYSTEM

Keeping pathogens out of the body. Skin and hair are a first line of defense in the **Immune System**.

Detecting touch, temperature, and pain. Skin is an important sensory organ, sending signals to be conveyed and interpreted by the **Nervous System**.

Delivering materials and wastes to and from the skin through blood vessels, which are part of the **Circulatory System**. These blood vessels also help regulate temperature.

Regulating many body functions through the glands in skin, which are part of the **Endocrine System**.

Interacting with the **Renal (or Urinary) System** to regulate water in the body. When someone sweats a lot, the kidneys produce less urine to conserve water.

Know Your Skin

Screensaver

Sunlight is made of electromagnetic waves, including **infrared*** radiation, visible light, and **ultraviolet*** radiation. Infrared and ultraviolet (UV) radiation are invisible. When infrared light hits the skin, it makes skin feel warm.

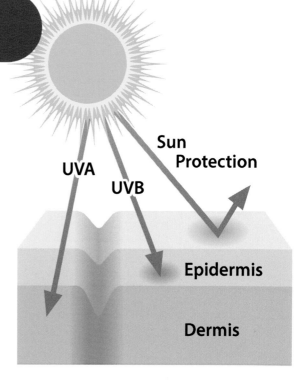

We need small amounts of UV radiation in order to produce vitamin D, which is important for your bone health, but too much UV light can be harmful. UV radiation is separated into three groups. The shortest wavelengths of UV radiation, UVC, are stopped by Earth's atmosphere. The middle wavelengths, UVB, mainly affect the epidermis. The longest wavelengths of UV radiation, UVA, reach deep into the dermis. About 95% of the UV radiation that reaches Earth's surface is UVA.

We protect ourselves from sunlight with hats and clothing, which provide the best protection. Sunglasses protect eyes, which are also vulnerable. Today, we have sunscreen, which is labeled with a Sun Protection Factor, or SPF. If applied correctly, a sunscreen with SPF 15 protects you from sunburn 15 times longer than without sunscreen.

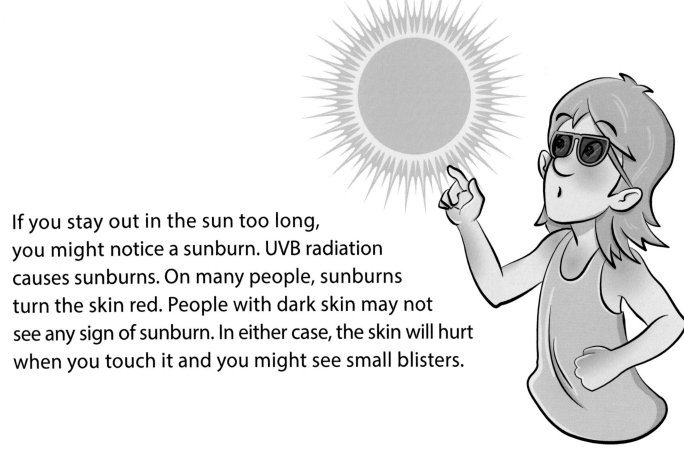

If you stay out in the sun too long, you might notice a sunburn. UVB radiation causes sunburns. On many people, sunburns turn the skin red. People with dark skin may not see any sign of sunburn. In either case, the skin will hurt when you touch it and you might see small blisters.

UV radiation, especially UVB radiation, damages DNA in skin cells. When this happens, skin cancer can result. The most common type of skin cancer is **carcinoma**,* which affects cells that don't contain melanin. Carcinomas are rarely fatal and can be removed with surgery. **Melanomas*** are a more serious type of skin cancer that affects melanocytes, or melanin-producing cells (find out about melanin on page 84). Melanomas grow quickly and can spread to other parts of the body—and can be fatal.

---

*Say them like this:

infrared - "in-fruh-**RED**"	**carcinoma** - "kar-sih-**NO**-muh"
ultraviolet - "ul-truh-**VIE**-oh-let"	**melanoma** - "mel-uh-**NO**-muh"

The strongest syllable is always shown in **CAPITALS** and **red**.

Know Your Skin

One of the best ways to reduce your chances of getting skin cancer, and other sun-related skin conditions, is by using sunscreen, wearing protective clothing, hats and sunglasses. Sunscreen should be applied as directed, and it should be reapplied frequently for the best protection. Sunscreen should also be applied on cloudy days.

No sunscreen is 100% effective against UV radiation.

You should try to limit your time in the sun, especially during the brightest parts of the day.

Braisin' in the Sun: Ancient Egyptians used rice bran, jasmine, and clays to try to protect their skin. Ancient Greeks used olive oil, which doesn't actually protect skin!

Warts and All

Since skin is your largest organ, taking care of it is super important! If you don't take care of your skin, it can lead to problems that can affect your health and your self-confidence.

The first step in caring for your skin is taking the time to get to know it. Is your skin dry or moist? Do you need to hydrate? Are there bumps that are trying to tell you what's going on below the surface? Do you sunburn easily? Can you recognize changes in the feeling and texture of your skin? Skin is our body's first line of defense so we better learn its language.

Clean skin is healthy skin so make sure you wash well—but not so often that you wash away the protective oil naturally present in your skin, called **sebum.*** Finally, in addition to sun protection, eating healthy, drinking plenty of water, and exercising will help keep your skin, hair, and nails healthy and vibrant.

Rashes, warts, acne, and other bumps are all possible signs that your skin needs attention. This is when it might be time to consult a dermatologist or another doctor who specializes in diseases of the skin.

***Say it like this:**

sebum - **"SEE**-bum**"**

The strongest syllable is always shown in **CAPITALS** and **red**.

Know Your Melanin

Color Real

Human skin, hair, and eyes comes in an incredible range of colors. **The pigment responsible for all of these shades is called melanin.***

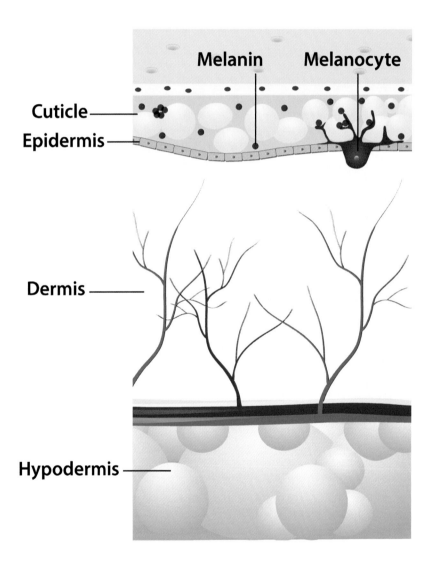

Cuticle

Epidermis

Melanin   Melanocyte

Dermis

Hypodermis

Your epidermis is filled with specialized cells called **melanocytes,*** which produce melanin. The pigment spreads to nearby cells, giving skin its color.

Regardless of the color of your skin, most humans have roughly the same number of melanocytes—it's just that some make more melanin than others.

People with darker skin have melanocytes that create more melanin, while people with fairer skin have melanocytes that create less.

Melanin naturally protects your skin from the sun. When ultraviolet light hits your skin, melanin absorbs the light, protecting your skin from burning to some extent.

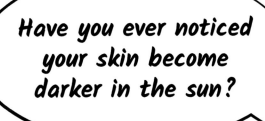

Have you ever noticed your skin become darker in the sun?

Increased sun exposure makes your melanocytes work overtime to release the extra melanin your skin needs to avoid damage from the sun.

Melanin is often unevenly distributed, adding to the uniqueness of each of our appearances. Freckles, for instance, are tiny pockets of skin where melanin accumulates. There are also less common variations, such as **vitiligo**,* a condition where melanocytes stop producing melanin, resulting in patches of white skin.

Some people have **albinism**,* meaning they have little to no melanin, making their skin extremely pale.

*Say them like this:

melanin - "mel-**UH**-nun"
melanocytes - "mel-**LAN**-oh-sites"

vitiligo - "vit-ill-**EYE**-go"
albinism - "**AL**-bin-is-em"

The strongest syllable is always shown in **CAPITALS** and **red**.

Know Your Surface Area

I'll Cover You

Your skin is the largest organ in your body. Just how big is your skin? Let's find out.

Materials:

- **Toilet paper**
- **Metric ruler**
- **A partner**

Directions:

1. Choose one person to wrap in toilet paper.

2. Gently wrap the person in toilet paper until they are completely covered — head, hands, and feet, too! Try not to let the toilet paper overlap too much. If the toilet paper tears, dispose of any partial squares. Then, start another strip with a new square.

3. Carefully remove all of the toilet paper. If you tear a square, keep all the pieces together. Lay the toilet paper flat on the floor or a table.

4. Count the number of toilet paper squares. Use a metric ruler to measure the length and width of a square in centimeters.

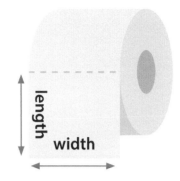

length

width

Complete the following chart to calculate the surface area of skin:

Calculate surface area of 1 toilet paper square	length ___ cm × width ___ cm = area of 1 square ___ cm²
Calculate total surface area	area of 1 square ___ cm² × ___ number of squares = total surface area ___ cm²
Convert to square meters	total surface area ___ cm² ÷ 10,000 = total surface area ___ m²

The surface area you just calculated is an estimate. How close do you think your calculation is to the actual measurement? Do you think it is larger or smaller than the actual surface area? Explain.

_____

_____

How big is skin? The average adult human has about 2 m² (21.5 ft²) of skin. Adult skin weighs 3.6 to 4.0 kg (8 to 9 lb).

Know Your Sensitivity

Ya Feel Me?

Skin helps you sense things about the world around you:

heat, cold, pain, pressure — your skin can sense it!

Just how sensitive is skin? Is it more sensitive in some places than others?

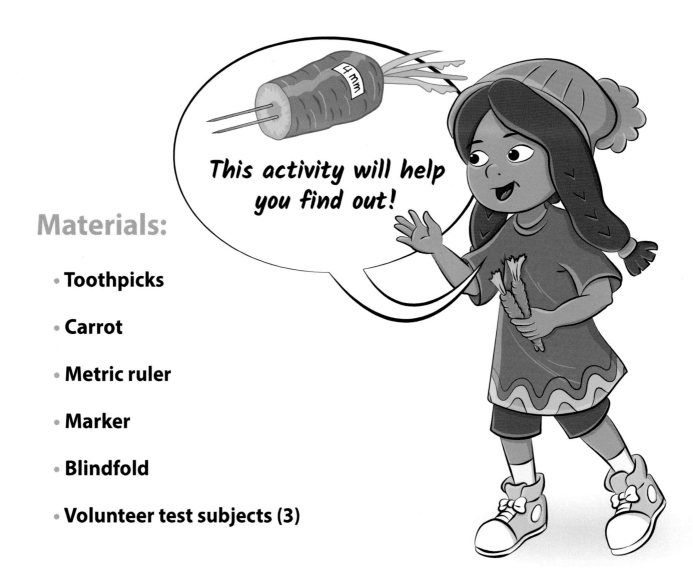

This activity will help you find out!

Materials:

- **Toothpicks**

- **Carrot**

- **Metric ruler**

- **Marker**

- **Blindfold**

- **Volunteer test subjects (3)**

Directions:

1. **Get an adult to cut the carrot** so that you have three cork-sized pieces.

2. Insert two toothpicks into the flat end of each piece of carrot. Use the metric ruler to measure the distance between the toothpicks. Space the toothpicks 4mm apart in one piece of carrot, 6mm apart in the next, then 8mm apart in the last one. Write the distance on each piece of carrot.

3. Blindfold your test subject. Have them sit with their arm relaxed on a table.

4. Test these areas: center of the palm, tip of the index finger, back of the hand, inside of the elbow, and upper arm. Using the carrot as a handle, touch the points of the toothpicks to the subject's skin very gently.

5. Ask the subject if they feel one point or two points on their skin. Repeat for each piece of carrot. Mark each answer "1" or "2," in the table below.

6. Repeat the process with the other two subjects.

Are some areas more sensitive than others?
Use your results to support your conclusion.

	SUBJECT 1			SUBJECT 2			SUBJECT 3		
mm between toothpicks	4	6	8	4	6	8	4	6	8
Palm									
Tip of index finger									
Back of hand									
Inside elbow									
Upper arm									

Know Your Fingerprints

Touch and Go

Ever wanted to solve a mystery? Remember how unique your fingerprints are? This game will teach you how to dust for fingerprints and learn the identity of a cookie thief!

Materials:

- **3 or more players**
- **White cardstock paper**
- **Black ink pad**
- **Clear glass jar with a twist off lid**
- **Glass cleaner**
- **Paper towel**
- **Gloves**
- **Cookie or other treat**
- **Notecards (sized 4 x 6 inches)**
- **Pen**
- **Bowl or hat**
- **Feathered paint brush**
- **Charcoal sticks, crushed into powder**
- **Cellophane tape**

Directions:

1. Give each player a piece of cardstock, this will be their "**Fingerprint Card**". Have them write their name at the top of the card. They will need to firmly press each finger on the ink pad and then onto the card so they leave a clear fingerprint. Make sure that they fill out prints for both hands.

2. Wipe down the outside of the glass jar completely with a cleaner and paper towel. You will want to wear gloves or handle the jar with the paper towel, so no fingerprints are left on the glass!

3. Carefully place a cookie inside the jar and put on the lid. Make sure no one touches the jar.

4. Make notecards for each of the players and fold them all in half twice. Write "**STEAL**" on one of the notecards. Then, place the folded cards into the bowl or hat.

5. Have each player draw a slip of paper from the bowl. Inform them that one person will get the "**STEAL**" slip, but they should keep it secret.

6. Everyone should go into a different room, away from the jar and the cookie.

FINGER TIP: It can be helpful for players to rub lotion into their hands before **Step 6**.

Know Your Fingerprints • Touch and Go

7. Give 5 minutes for the player who got the "**STEAL**" slip to sneak into the room with the jar, remove the lid, and steal the cookie. They can eat the evidence!

8. Now check the jar. Is the cookie gone? Then it's time to dust for prints!

9. Put on your gloves and rub the brush lightly into the charcoal powder.

10. Gently dust the brush over the jar. You should see some fingerprints appear! The charcoal is sticking to the sweat and oils from the thief's fingers.

FINGER TIP: Dusting for fingerprints can get messy! Put some newspaper down first and be ready to clean up afterward.

11. Cut a piece of cellophane tape and carefully place it over one of the fingerprints.

12. Peel the cellophane tape off the glass and place it on a fresh note card.

13. Repeat steps 11 and 12 until you have collected samples of all the fingerprints.

14. Compare the fingerprints you've collected to the Fingerprint Cards. Can you figure out which player stole the cookie?

Look for these patterns in the fingerprints:

FINGER TIP: Take a photo with a smartphone so you can enlarge the image. This way you'll get to zoom in and get a better look at print details.

Now that you know how to dust for fingerprints, **what mysteries can you solve in your own home?**

_____

_____

_____

_____

Where will you find a lot of different fingerprints?

_____

_____

_____

Where do you think you'll find just one person's fingerprints?

_____

_____

_____

Mole Patrol

Remember how your epidermis is filled with specialized cells called melanocytes, which produce melanin and give you your skin pigment?

A mole is a collection of melanocytes.

You may have seen one before and saw that it was flat or rounded and raised outside of the skin's surface. Moles can also be other shapes and sometimes they even have hair growing outside of them.

Most of the time, moles are perfectly normal! In some rare instances, a mole can become cancerous. One way to see if a mole is healthy or may require a professional opinion is to do an at-home visual check. To do this, make sure the mole is symmetrical on both sides and that over time, the shape of the mole stays the same. You can eyeball the mole, or take a magnifying glass or hand mirror out for fun!

Materials:

- **Magnifying glass**

- **Hand mirror**

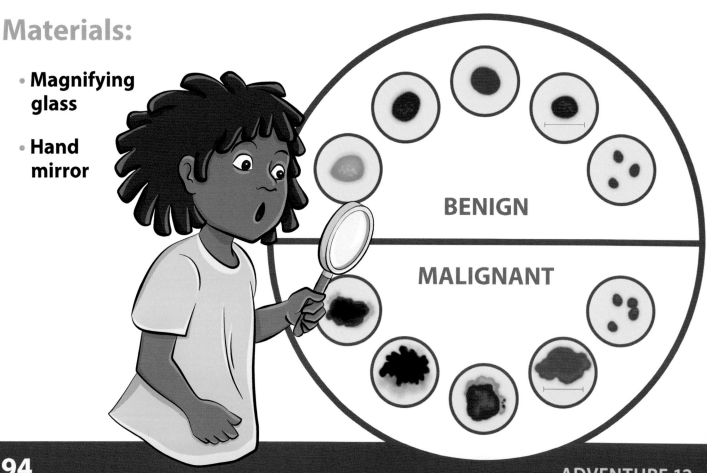

Acne Acumen

Acne is a skin disorder that happens when a hair follicle and gland gets clogged up with **sebum** (the oily, waxy substance that appears on our skin), dead skin cells, or bacteria. It's the most common skin condition in the United States and you can get it at any age, but it's generally known as something that happens in your teens. Studies in the US show around 85% of people experience at least minor acne between the ages of 12 and 24.

Do you or someone that you know have acne?

You most often will see it on someone's face, but acne can also pop up on a person's back, chest, and shoulders.

Most commonly, acne is experienced by teens and young adults. **Acne can be embarrassing, so practice kindness when you or someone you know has acne.** Finding a solution is not always simple, but seeing a licensed dermatologist can help.

Try taking a look at your own pores using a highly magnified mirror or at someone else's pores using a magnifying glass.

What do you see when you stare up close at the face?

Can you see an individual pore and hair follicle?

Materials:

- **Highly magnified mirror**

- **Magnifying glass**

Strand at Hand

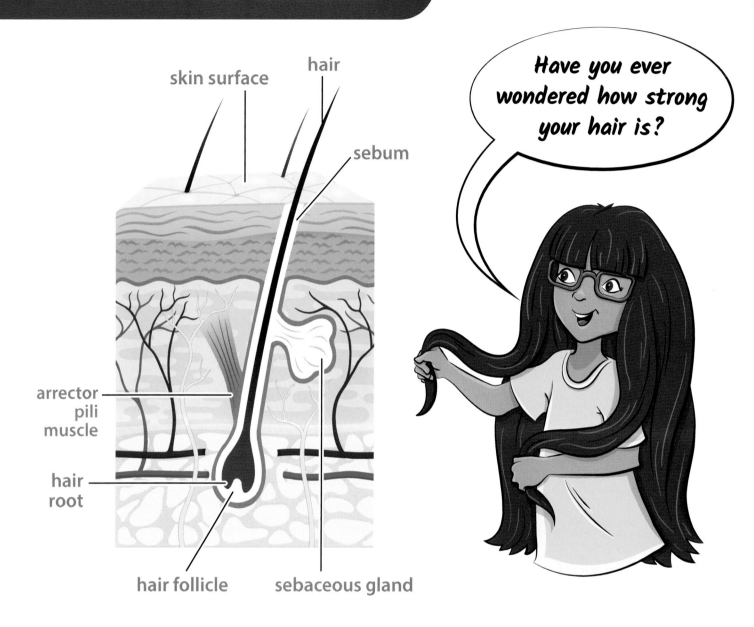

skin surface

hair

sebum

arrector pili muscle

hair root

hair follicle

sebaceous gland

Have you ever wondered how strong your hair is?

If you have combed your hair and felt your comb tug on a knot, you might have felt concerned about the strength of your hair. Even if you have not, it might still be fun to know just how strong your hair is exactly. Care to put your hair to the test?

Hair texture and strength is reflective of melanin in your skin, genetics, and nutrition that is unique to every individual person. Hair strength is just that — the strength of a hair strand. Have fun testing out the strength of your hair using the home inventory materials and the directions in the next page!

Materials:

- **Ziploc® bag**
- **Paperclip**
- **A strand of your hair**
- **A desk or table**
- **Tape**
- **Pennies**
- **Paper**
- **Pen**
- **Magnifying glass** (optional)

Directions:

1. Take your Ziploc® bag and unseal it so the top is open.

2. Grab the paper clip. Below the center of the seal area of the Ziploc®, push one end of the paperclip into one side of the bag.

3. Next, you will need to fasten your hair strand to the opposite end of the paper clip. You can do this by fastening a knot around it. If your hair is shorter, apply tape instead.

4. Locate a table or desk. Find where the Ziploc® hangs off the edge and your hair can rest on the table. Then, tape your hair to the desk or table securely.

5. Drop a penny into the bag to test your hairs strength. Keep adding pennies until the hair breaks. Once it does, count all the pennies.

6. How many pennies do you have? Write this number down. Using the penny total, multiply by .088 ounces (this is the weight of a penny). Now you know how many ounces just one strand of your hair can hold!

> **Bonus:** For a little extra challenge, try taking a few hair samples from other members of your household (pets included!). Compare your findings for each hair. If you look at the hairs underneath a magnifying glass, can you see any similarities or differences?

Serve the People, Body and Soul

Our integumentary system holds our body together and keeps it safe, much like a community can come together to keep its members safe. Skin shelters you from pathogens and the sun, but it also makes Vitamin D; hair and nails protect your head, fingers, and toes.

As you'll see at the comic in the end of this book, K-Dub's encouragement to build the skate park is just like asking the integumentary system to do its job: it will require the whole community to come together in support of the effort. Not only that, but to come together over the course of time, not only in one instant.

Just like if the skin gets broken and skin cells decide to not help repair the skin, if the community doesn't provide maintenance to the skate park, it will deteriorate overtime.

Think about your community.
Identify some of the things your community needs and try to come up with an idea that might help fix them.

Need: _____

_____

Idea: _____

_____

Need: _____

_____

Idea: _____

_____

Need: _____

_____

Idea: _____

_____

Integumentary Investigation

INTEGUMENTARY

EPIDERMIS

COLLAGEN

ELASTIN

ARRECTOR PILI

MECHANORECEPTORS

THERMORECEPTORS

NOCICEPTORS

HOMEOSTASIS

CARCINOMA

MELANOMA

SEBUM

MELANIN

MELANOCYTES

ULTRAVIOLET

Answer keys on page 129.

```
N M D I U E P I D E R M I S H R K A
O M E C H A N O R E C E P T O R S R
C M E L A N O C Y T E S E B U M M R
I C O L L A G E N C S I Q A R T M E
C A R C I N O M A Q W H I L G J G C
E S B A P Q F X B F Q E T T Z J C T
P P U S Q B P A M E L A N O M A F O
T T I N T E G U M E N T A R Y C L R
O T H E R M O R E C E P T O R S O P
R E L A S T I N Y M E L A N I N V I
S T K V H O M E O S T A S I S K R L
L A U L T R A V I O L E T R Z E W I
```

Systems Security

Good work, adventurers!

Now that you know the integumentary system, let's review what you've learned!

Try to fill in the blanks.

In this guide, you learned about the integumentary system,

which is made up of your ___ ___ ___ ___ ___ , ___ ___ ___ ___ ___ , and ___ ___ ___ ___ ___ ___ .

This system serves you by keeping out ___ ___ ___ ___ ___ ___ ___ ___ ___ ___ ___ ,

regulating your body ___ ___ ___ ___ ___ ___ ___ ___ ___ ___ ___ ___ ,

sensing your ___ ___ ___ ___ ___ ___ ___ ___ ___ ___ ___ ___ , and removing ___ ___ ___ ___ ___ ___ .

Your ___ ___ ___ ___ is the largest organ of the integumentary system.

Inside of the skin, there are ___ ___ ___ ___ ___ main layers: the epidermis,

___ ___ ___ ___ ___ ___ , and the ___ ___ ___ ___ ___ ___ ___ ___ ___ ___ ___ layer.

Pigment is what you see when you notice the range of human skin colors,

the incredible array you see is made possible by __ __ __ __ __ __ __ __.

The more melanin in your skin, means the more protection you have from

the sun's __ __ light.

While a small amount of UV radiation is needed for you to produce vitamin __ ,

too much sunlight can cause __ __ __ __ __ __ __ , and even skin cancer!

Luckily, the broad spectrum __ __ __ __ __ __ __ __ __ that protects from UVA

and UVB rays can offer some skin defense.

Ready to verify what you have learned?
See the answer key on page 130!

Know Your Appetite

Southern Comfort

Many Southern cuisines were developed by Black cooks and chefs in the kitchens of the Southern United States. Reaching from Virginia to Florida to Texas, "the South" often includes Louisiana through both North and South Carolina. These regions had a variety of influences, growing a food culture with elements from Native Americans and people from Europe and West and Central Africa.

One famous dish from the Low country region of South Carolina is Hoppin' John, a mixture of black-eyed peas and other vegetables served with rice. Its name possibly came from the Haitian Creole, **pois à pigeon**,* heard as "Hoppin' John." Served with collard greens and cornbread, it's eaten on New Year's Day to ensure a prosperous year ahead.

Buttery pound cake is a beloved dessert, named after its original, easy-to-remember recipe: one pound each of butter, sugar, eggs, and flour.

Pinky's Hint:

Read through the entire recipe before beginning to prepare food. This way, you'll know what equipment and ingredients are needed, and you'll be familiar with the steps involved.

 Whenever you see the chef's hat icon, it means **you'll need an adult's help**.

To many, Southern cuisine is the **epitome*** (perfect example) of good, delicious, home cooking. Its focus on seasonal and local ingredients, vegetables flavored with meat and spices, and abundance created from scarcity make it a favorite comfort food all over the world.

*Say them like this:

pois à pigeon - "pwa-pee-**ZHAWN**"
epitome - "ih-**PIT**-uh-me"

The strongest syllable is always shown in **CAPITALS** and **red**.

Recipes and food knowledge provided by
Chef Polly Legendre of La Gourmande Catering.

Hoppin' John

Makes 2-4 servings

Prep time: 20 minutes

Cook time: 30 minutes

Ingredients:

- 4 cloves garlic
- 1 small bunch green onions or 1 medium yellow onion
- 1 green bell pepper, seeded
- 2 celery stalks
- 2 tablespoon vegetable oil
- 1 can (15 oz) black-eyed peas
- 1 cup chopped tomatoes (or 14.5 ounces canned, peeled, whole tomatoes)
- 1 cup vegetable broth
- salt and pepper, to taste
- red pepper flakes (optional, to taste)
- 2 tablespoon chopped parsley (optional, for garnish)
- 2 to 3 cups of cooked rice

Preparation:

 1. Finely chop the garlic, onion, celery, and green bell pepper.

 2. In a skillet, heat the vegetable oil and gently sauté the garlic, then the onion, until fragrant. Add the celery and green pepper and sauté until tender.

 3. Drain and rinse the black-eyed peas. Add them, along with the tomatoes, to the vegetables and season with salt, pepper, and/or pepper flakes. Mix in the broth and bring everything to a simmer.

4. Cook for 15 minutes then season with salt and pepper to taste. If using parsley, sprinkle it over the top of the Hoppin' John to added color.

5. Serve the Hoppin' John over cooked rice.

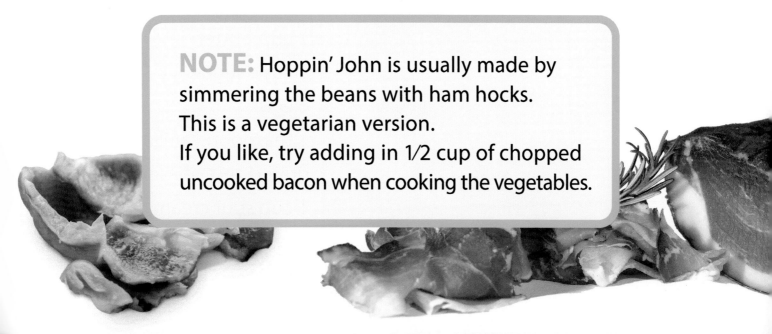

NOTE: Hoppin' John is usually made by simmering the beans with ham hocks. This is a vegetarian version. If you like, try adding in 1/2 cup of chopped uncooked bacon when cooking the vegetables.

Lemon Sour Cream Pound Cake

**Makes approximately
16 1-inch slices**

**Prep time:
30 minutes**

**Cook time:
1 hour**

Ingredients:

- 3 cups flour
- 1/2 teaspoon baking powder
- 1/4 teaspoon baking soda
- 1/2 teaspoon salt
- 1 cup butter
- 3 cups sugar
- 6 eggs
- 1 teaspoon vanilla
- grated zest of 2 lemons
- 1 cup sour cream
- powdered sugar to dust on top

Preparation:

1. Position a rack in the center of the oven and preheat to 325°F.

2. Spread a thin layer of butter on the inside of a 10-inch fluted tube (Bundt) pan, or an 8-inch round cake pan, or 2 loaf pans. Add a few tablespoons of flour and move the pan around so that the flour coats the butter. Then tap out the excess flour.

3. Combine the flour, baking powder, baking soda, and salt together; set aside.

4. Beat the butter, sugar, vanilla and lemon zest in a large bowl with a hand-held electric mixer on high speed until light and fluffy. This should take about 3 minutes.

5. Beat in the eggs, adding them one at a time.

6. On low speed, add the flour in 3 additions, alternating with 2 additions of the sour cream, beginning and ending with the flour. Beat until smooth, scraping down the sides of the bowl often with a rubber spatula.

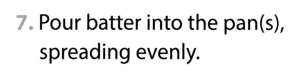

7. Pour batter into the pan(s), spreading evenly.

8. Bake until a knife or wooden skewer inserted in the center of the cake comes out clean, about 1 hour.

9. When the cake is ready, remove from the oven and let cool on a wire rack.

10. When cool, turn the cake pan over to gently remove from the pan. Set it on a serving plate right-side up and dust lightly with powdered sugar. **It's ready to serve!**

Fire in the Belly:

Part cookbook, part memoir, "The Taste of Country Cooking" was one of the first to popularize Southern cooking. Author and acclaimed chef Edna Lewis grew up in a Virginia farming community, where her grandparents—former slaves—taught her to cook, hunt, forage, harvest, and prepare all manners of food from the land. A culinary **luminary** (person of prominence or brilliant achievement), Lewis has inspired generations of chefs.

*Say it like this:

luminary - **"LOO**-mih-nare-ee**"

The strongest syllable is always shown in **CAPITALS** and **red**.

 Show off your cooking skills!

Have your grown up take a photo, and share on social media using the hashtag:

#KnowYourAdventure

 KnowYourselfOAK   **KnowYourselfOAK**

Vast Food

Go out to dinner in Oakland, California, and you might find fried catfish, collard greens, cornbread, and sweet potato pie on the menu. How did food that originated in the American South make it all the way to Northern California?

When African-American families left the South during the Great Migration, they brought their favorite recipes. Some moved to the Bay Area and opened restaurants, often serving the same dishes they enjoyed in places like Tennessee, Alabama, or Kentucky.

What we know as soul food is deeply rooted in Southern cooking and African-American history. Often given limited ingredients to cook with (for example, corn, sweet potatoes, leftover cuts of meat, and molasses), slaves had to fish, grow, or hunt anything else themselves. Combining African cooking techniques with new ones, they figured out the best ways to prepare and season food.

Creativity continues to be a hallmark of Southern Black cuisine. As African-Americans moved to other parts of the country, they adopted aspects of Chinese, Italian, and Mexican food—just as Southern cooking had drawn inspiration from Native American, European, and African dishes. In the 1960s, the term "soul food" was coined to describe this combined culinary tradition and emphasize that Black Americans had a very different cultural experience with these foods than their Southern white neighbors did.

Think about the special recipes in your own family and community. **Are they from a specific time or part of the world? Have they changed?**

_____

_____

_____

Would any ingredients be hard to find?

_____

_____

_____

If someone wasn't familiar with the dish and tried to prepare it, how might it be different?

_____

_____

_____

TASTE QUEST: Check out the types of restaurants in the city where you live. In some places, you'll see several kinds of food on one street!

Positively Powerful

Hello Adventurers!

In this guide, you learned about the Integumentary System.

What are some things that you can do to help keep your hair, skin, and nails healthy?

_____

_____

_____

_____

_____

_____

_____

_____

_____

Throughout the Adventure we learned that hair is a way to express yourself.

What are some other ways that you express yourself?

_____

_____

_____

_____

_____

_____

_____

_____

_____

_____

Positively Powerful

(continuation)

Our integumentary system holds our body together and keeps it safe, much like a community can come together and keep its members safe.

What is an example of one way you've seen people in your community come together to solve a problem?

_____

_____

_____

_____

_____

_____

_____

_____

Has the solution worked?

_____

_____

_____

_____

_____

_____

How would you try to fix the issue?

_____

_____

_____

_____

_____

THE SEVENTH SENSE

Wait...

Since when does Hank get haircuts?

Further Reading

Nonfiction for Younger Readers

- This book contains beautiful illustrations using eye-catching x-rays, diagrams, and more to peak young reader's interest in the human body. Seymour Simon is an award-winning author of children's science literature.

Simon, Seymour.
The Human Body. HarperCollins Publishers, 2008. **(ages 6-10)**

Fiction for Older Readers

- Telling the story of three sisters who travel to Oakland in 1968 to find their mother, this historical fiction blends a compelling personal story with the historical setting of a very tumultuous time for the civil rights movement.

Williams-Garcia, Rita.
One Crazy Summer. United States, Quill Tree Books, 2010. **(ages 9-12)**

Fiction for All Readers

- Author, Dr. Arlisha Norwood engages young learners interested in learning more about Black history. In her book she features the stories of 51 Black leaders and provides additional resources for kids to continue learning about their Black hero.

Norwood, Arlisha.
Black Heroes: A Black History Book for Kids: 51 Inspiring People from Ancient Africa to Modern-Day U.S.A. Rockridge Press, 2020. **(ages 8-13)**

Adventure Series Workbooks

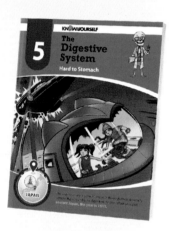

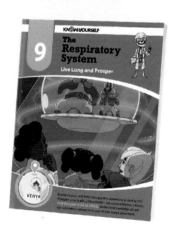

The **Adventure Series Workbooks** introduces 12 systems of the human body to build a foundation for human anatomy. Created to eliminate the mystery kids face when it comes to their bodies, the **Know Yourself Adventure Series** provides entertaining and educational tools that help children become masters of how their minds and bodies work – a process we call "self-literacy."

knowyourself.com

K-Dub

K-Dub is a Father, Artist, Educator and Action Sports Activist in Oakland, CA.

What inspires you?
I'm inspired by our youth, the times, and the amazingly talented folks in the Bay Area.

Message to readers
First, think about ways to uplift your family either through education or hard work and effort. Develop work habits with discipline those elements with a pay off later.

Did you know:
The Loops Crew were named from a skateboard wheel project (Loops Wheels) that was developed to Gift Back to local youth. The name just seem to fit the characters as they were always rolling into some new adventure.

If we were to describe K-Dub in one word: Inspiring

Answer Keys

Operation Oakland

Crossword answers:

- 1 Down: BREAKFAST
- 2 Down: MADAM WALKER
- 3 Down: DISCRIMINATION
- 4 Down: KWAME
- 5 Across: BEEHIVE
- 6 Across: OAKLAND
- 7 Across: CALIFORNIA
- 8 Across: THE GREAT MIGRATION
- 9 Down: JIM CROW LAWS
- 10 Across: NO SWEAT

Integumentary Investigation

```
N M D I U E P I D E R M I S H R K A
O M E C H A N O R E C E P T O R S R
C M E L A N O C Y T E S E B U M M R
I C O L L A G E N C S I Q A R T M E
C A R C I N O M A Q W H I L G J G C
E S B A P Q F X B F Q E T T Z J C T
P P U S Q B P A M E L A N O M A F O
T T I N T E G U M E N T A R Y C L R
O T H E R M O R E C E P T O R S O P
R E L A S T I N Y M E L A N I N V I
S T K V H O M E O S T A S I S K R L
L A U L T R A V I O L E T R Z E W I
```

Answer Keys

Systems Security

In this guide, you learned about the integumentary system, which is made up of your h a i r , s k i n , and n a i l s . This system serves you by keeping out p a t h o g e n s , regulating your body t e m p e r a t u r e , sensing your e n v i r o n m e n t , and removing w a s t e .

Your s k i n is the largest organ of the integumentary system. Inside of the skin, there are t h r e e main layers: the epidermis, d e r m i s , and the s u b c u t a n e o u s layer. Pigment is what you see when you notice the range of human skin colors, the incredible array you see is made possible by m e l a n i n . The more melanin in your skin, means the more protection you have from the sun's U V light.

While a small amount of UV radiation is needed for you to produce vitamin D , too much sunlight can cause s u n b u r n , and even skin cancer! Luckily, the broad spectrum s u n s c r e e n that protects from UVA and UVB rays can offer some skin defense.

CREATED WITH LOVE

BY THE

KNOW YOURSELF TEAM